Tana Hoban

Dots, Spots, Speckles, and Stripes

GREENWILLOW BOOKS, New York

The photographs were reproduced from 35-mm slides
and printed in full color.

Library of Congress Cataloging-in-Publication Data
Hoban, Tana.   Dots, spots, speckles, and stripes.
Summary: Photographs show dots, spots, speckles, and stripes as
found on clothing, flowers, faces, animals, and other places.
1. Form perception—Juvenile literature.
[1. Shape.   2. Form perception]   I. Title.
BF293.H62 1987   152.1'423   86-22919
ISBN 0-688-06862-6   ISBN 0-688-06863-4 (lib. bdg.)

For Miela and Bob,
Max and Jen
——where this book began